The Runaway Tractor

Heather Amery

Illustrated by Stephen Cartwright

Language consultant: Betty Root
Series editor: Jenny Tyler

How to use this book

This book tells a story about the Boot family who live on Apple Tree Farm.
Some words in the story have been replaced by pictures.
Find the stickers that match these pictures and stick them over the top.
Each sticker has the word with it to help you read the story.

Some of the big pictures have pieces missing.
Find the stickers with the missing pieces to finish the pictures.

A yellow duck is hidden in every picture. When you have found
the duck you can put a sticker on the page.

This is Apple Tree Farm.

Mrs. Boot, the farmer, has two 

called Poppy and Sam. She also has a

called Rusty.

Ted works on the farm.

He drives a red 

. He has filled the trailer with hay. He is taking it to the fields to feed the hungry 

.

Poppy and Sam are playing in the barn.

"Listen," says 

. "I can hear Ted shouting,

and the tractor is making a funny noise."

"What can it be?" says 

.

Poppy and Sam run to the gate.

The tractor is racing down the hill.

watches it. The

goes

faster and faster. "It won't stop," shouts Ted.

The trailer comes off.

It runs down the hill and crashes into a 

.

The 

tips up and all the hay

falls out. The tractor is still racing down the hill.

The tractor runs into the duck pond.

It hits the  with a splash. The engine

makes a loud noise, then it stops with a long hiss.

The  fly away.

Poppy and Sam run down the hill.

Ted climbs out of the 

.

The water comes to the top of his boots.

The 

look at the tractor.

Ted looks worried.

He takes off his 

and tips out the water. His 

are soaking wet.

How can he get the tractor out of the pond?

"Go and find your mother, please."

"Ask her to fetch Farmer Dray," says 

.

"He might be able to help." Poppy and Sam

run back to the 

.

Farmer Dray brings his horse.

Her name is Dolly. She has a long, black 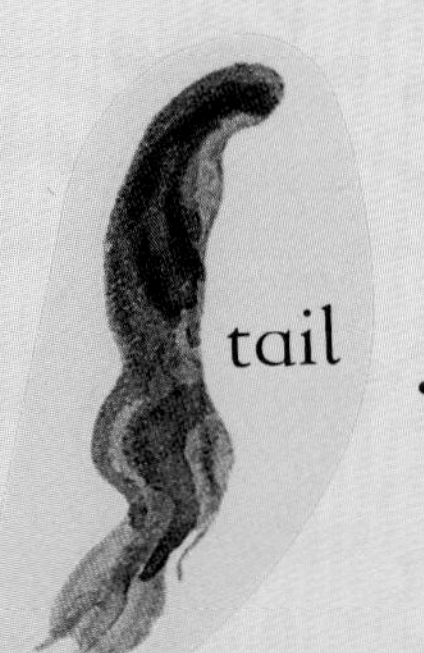

.

Dolly is a cart 

, so she is

very strong. She will help Ted.

Farmer Dray has brought a long rope.

He ties the  to the horse.

rope

Ted ties the other end to the tractor. "Now we are ready," says  .

Farmer Dray

Dolly pulls and pulls.

The tractor is very heavy. 

pushes as hard as he can. Very slowly the 

start to move.

Ted's hands are wet.

His  start slipping. The tractor jerks

forward and Ted falls in the water. His 

falls off. Now he is very wet and muddy.

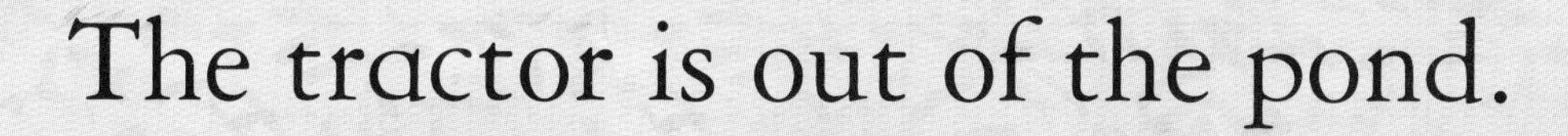

The tractor is out of the pond.

Farmer Dray unties the  .

rope

"We must leave the  to dry,"

tractor

says Ted. "And I must get dry too."

Farmer Dray, Poppy and Sam ride home.

Ted blows his nose on his  .

He is so muddy he has to walk home.

Cover design by Vici Leyhane   Digital manipulation by Nelupa Hussain

This edition first published in 2004 by Usborne Publishing Ltd, Usborne House, 83-85 Saffron Hill, London EC1N 8RT, England. www.usborne.com

 First published in America in 2004. U.E. Printed in Malaysia.